D1207263

I Can Pray

Published by Caldwell Ministries, Inc.
6011 West Orem Drive
Houston, TX 77085

Copyright © 2013 by Suzette T. Caldwell
prayerinstitute.com

All rights reserved.
No part of this book may be reproduced or transmitted in any form
or by any means, electronic or mechanical, including
photocopying, recording or by any information storage
and retrieval system, without the written permission
of the Publisher, except where permitted by law.

Manufactured in the United States of America

Illustrated by Nikkolas Smith

Library of Congress Cataloging in Publication Data

ISBN – 978-0-9828041-4-8

Daisy

Tan Lee

Suzy

KJ

Marisol

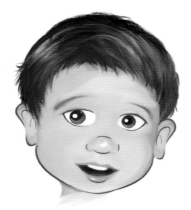

Burgess

Written By **Suzette T. Caldwell**

Illustrated By **Nikkolas Smith**

"I can hit a ball..."

"I can draw
a macaw..."

2

"I can sip milk through a straw..."

3

"I can walk on my  tippy toes..."

"I can smell a rose..."

"I CAN PRAY!"

8

"I can count to ten…"

1 2 3 4
5 6 7
8 9
10

9

"I can write my name with a pen..."

Marisol

Write Your Name!

1

2

3

"I can stand at attention..."

11

"I Can Pray!"

12

"I can reach for the stars..."

13

"I can eat cookies from a jar..."

15

"I can clean up
my room..."

17

"I can blow up a balloon…"

18

"I can whistle a happy tune…"

"I can swing up high... "

21

"I can wink my left eye..."

"I can make a mud pie..."

23

"I CAN PRAY!!!"

24

"I can say my ABC's..."

"I can buzzzzz like 100 bees..."

26

"I CAN PRAY!"

28

"I can do the bunny hop..."

"I can lick a lollipop..."

"I can grocery shop..."

31

"So, listen as I say,
The words that Jesus gave..."
...and then you too
will know how
to pray!"

33

"Our Father, who art in heaven,
hallowed be thy name..."

34

" Thy Kingdom come, thy will be done,
on Earth as it is in Heaven. "

35

"Give us this day, our daily bread... "

36

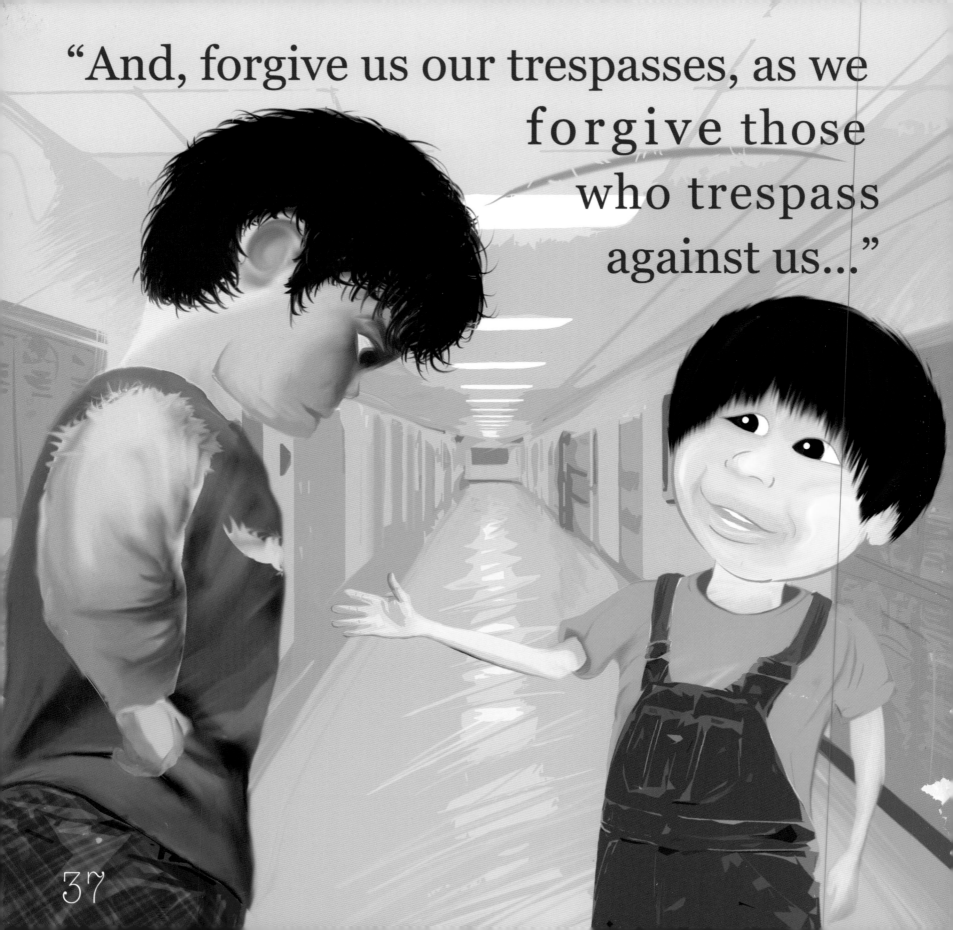

"And help us not to yield to temptation, but deliver us from the evil one." 38

"For thine is the Kingdom, the power, and the glory, forever! AMEN!!!"

"I CAN PRAY !!!"